In The Beginning, God Said.
Eat Raw Food
Genesis 1:29......A Closer Look

William D. Scott

**Published by
North Idaho Publishing
Coeur d'Alene, Idaho**

Distributed By:
www.raw-food.com
POB 900202, SD, CA 92190
800-205-2350

In The Beginning, God Said.
Eat Raw Food
Genesis 1:29......A Closer Look

By William D. Scott

Published by:

North Idaho Publishing
Post Office Box 2833
Coeur d'Alene, ID 83816-2833 U.S.A.

ISBN 0-9676286-0-1

Library of Congress Card Number: 99-091304

Printed in the United States of America by Morris Publishing
3212 East Highway 30 • Kearney, Nebraska 68847 • 800-650-7888

TABLE OF CONTENTS

ABOUT THE AUTHOR

Raised in Lynwood, which is in Southern California, Bill is a fourth generation Seventh-day Adventist with a strong medical tradition in his family. Both his grandfathers were medical doctors as is his father. All were graduates of the College of Medical Evangelists which later became Loma Linda University.

He attended Lynwood S.D.A. Elementary School and from there went to Lynwood Academy graduating in 1961. Having been influenced by the long hours his father spent in the practice of medicine, he then enrolled at La Sierra College as a Biology major with emphasis on pre-dental requirements. The summer of 1965 found him graduating from La Sierra College and moving to Loma Linda where he began his freshman year at Loma Linda University Dental School.

Four years later upon graduating from dental school he married Karen Fillmore, a sister of two other dental students, whom he met during his senior year of dentistry. They moved to Central California and opened a general practice dental office in Porterville, California. Life was basically normal and uneventful for them. Children arrived a couple years apart, a girl first then a boy and everything went along as expected.

After eleven years of general practice, Bill returned to L.L.U. Dental School in pursuit of a Masters Degree in Orthodontics. After graduating in 1982 they moved to Modesto, California and opened the doors to a new dental practice specializing in Orthodontics. Lots of hard work and time spent found the practice thriving and growing every year. Five years after opening the orthodontic office, however, unbeknownst to them things were suddenly going to change dramatically.

Please continue reading for the rest of that story.

They are now living happily in Coeur d'Alene, Idaho.

Acknowledgments

To Karen, Janelle, and Dennis for their love and support in various spoken and unspoken ways during a critical time of my life.

To Karen for her support and encouragement during our study, from which the idea for this book took root and grew.

To Lin and Bj, especially for their friendship, for all their encouragement, suggestions, and time spent reading and correcting all my many errors.

Without their help and encouragement, this book would not have been possible.

Disclaimer

The nutritional and health information in this book is based on the teachings of God's Holy Word—the Bible, as well as personal experience and research. The author and publisher do not offer medical advice or prescribe the use of diet as a form of treatment for sickness without the approval of a health professional. Because there is always some risk involved when changing diet and lifestyles, the author and publisher cannot be responsible for any adverse consequences or detoxification effects resulting from the use of any procedures or dietary suggestions described hereafter. Only apply the information in this book if you are willing to assume responsibility. If you do use the information contained in this book without the approval of a health professional, you are prescribing for yourself, which is your constitutional right, but the author and publisher assume no responsibility.

Introduction

In our walk down this path of life it took some severe and near-fatal events to remind us of the fact that we needed God. It showed us the **critical necessity** to study God's word for ourselves in order to come to a **personal understanding** of what He wants for us. Ellen White says it so well:

> God's people are not prepared for the loud cry
> of the third angel. They have a work to do for
> themselves which they should not leave for God to
> do for them. He has left this work for them to do.
> It is an individual work; one cannot do it for
> another. (*Testimonies For The Church*, Vol. 1, p. 486)
> (*Counsels on Diet and Foods*, p. 32)

The importance of it being an individual work cannot be overstated!

It is my hope and prayer that this book will encourage you to study for yourselves these issues that have become steeped in Adventist tradition, and to find God's way for yourself. At the same time if it helps you avoid some of the pitfalls we encountered along this path, we would praise God for giving you the desire to study and learn His way.

* * * * * * * * * * *

19 For the wisdom of this world is foolishness
with God. For it is written, He taketh the wise
in their own craftiness. (*I Corinthians* 3:19)

God has formed laws which govern our constitutions, and these laws which He has placed in our being are divine, and for every transgression there is affixed a penalty, which must sooner or later be realized. The majority of diseases which the human family have been and still are suffering under, they have created by ignorance of their own organic laws. They seem indifferent in regard to the matter of health, and work perseveringly to tear themselves to pieces, and when broken down and debilitated in body and mind, send for the doctor and drug themselves to death.

(*Health Reformer*, October, 1866)
(*Counsels on Diet and Foods*, p. 19)

Chapter One

Our Awakening

Cerebral Aneurysm

It started out like most other work days with the hustle and bustle of two children getting ready for school. Their Mom and I were helping them as necessary while at the same time preparing ourselves for a busy day. My schedule at the office that Tuesday was especially busy in the morning because the afternoon was blocked off for a computer training session for my employees. I was looking forward to a relaxing afternoon working on a remodeling project of our home.

Time passed quickly as I cut boards for backing and bracing then climbed up and down the ladder nailing them into place. Sooner than expected I heard Karen drive away to pick up our son from a friend's house. It was already 4:00 pm or so. After climbing down the ladder I bent over to pick up the next board and my head was instantaneously screaming at me with a sudden severe headache. It felt ready to burst. Quickly straightening up my first thought, "Is this it?" crossed my mind as I noticed my eyesight failing me. Within seconds the lower half of my body went totally numb and then I realized, "Yes, this **is** it!" Panic enveloped me and wild thoughts raced through my mind, such as: "I'm dying.... I need help.... there's nothing I can do now to get saved.... It's too late for me.... I'm dying now...." Instinctively, I knew this panic wasn't helping me so I began to calm myself down by breathing slow and easy, and trying to stay relaxed. So, there I stood, sightless, with my head feeling ready to explode, total numbness from the waist down, and I'm telling myself to keep calm!

After a short period of time the headache began to improve. My eyesight was returning as was the feeling in the lower half of my body. Not wanting to fall or let my head drop again caused me to stand still until I thought I could move about safely. I slowly made my way downstairs to a part of the house where my wife would find me when she came home. I began wondering, "How would I tell her?"

Here I was, a forty-four year old orthodontist in the prime of life, with what was, by worldly standards, a great life. Two wonderful children, ages twelve and fourteen, and my wife and best friend, Karen, were all depending on me. We had become accustomed to the lifestyle of a family with higher than average income. At the same time, we were not really interested in "church" things, but went to church nonetheless "for the kids." In looking around us our religious experience didn't seem that much different from those we saw at church. Suddenly, many of the things that seemed so important at one point in my life no longer had much meaning.

While waiting for Karen to come home that fateful day I was wondering what would happen next. With my educational background, I was guessing that I had experienced a ruptured cerebral aneurysm and my thoughts were focused on what I would be able to do in the future. Should I, or could I, ever go back to work, ever water or snow ski again, or even play catch with my kids in the yard? At that point, with my limited knowledge about aneurysms, I didn't think anything could be done about my problem. I was preparing myself to live what life I had left with the threat of another rupture occurring at any time.

By the time Karen arrived home I still had not thought of a way to gently tell her what had happened. Until now I only had to deal with my own thoughts and emotions. Upon seeing her I realized many other factors would now be part of this, not the least of which was my emotional state at that time. I debated whether to tell her or not, but finally called to her saying "something happened I need to tell you about." Without using the word aneurysm I told her very briefly what had happened and that I thought I might have had a blood vessel in my head "bleed a little bit."

Over my objections she called a medical doctor friend of ours that lived a few doors down the street. I didn't want to bother him after hours and thought I could just "go in tomorrow to be checked." She insisted, however, and that was a critical decision. He arrived within a few minutes and after checking me and listening to my explanation of what had transpired, he confirmed my feelings about what had happened. Much to my surprise he said I needed to get to the hospital right away for tests, because some of these aneurysms could be repaired. For a brief moment hope flooded into me. Suddenly it hit me, however, that it would probably require brain surgery to repair this, so my hope was quickly replaced with fear and dread.

Hospital tests confirmed that I had a cerebral aneurysm at the base of my brain on the anterior communicating artery. The neurosurgeon explained the options and the risks associated with each. It was decided the only viable treatment was surgery. Scheduled for as early as possible the next day I began preparing myself mentally for the ordeal that would follow and I prayed for God's presence in my heart and in the operating room. The surgeon had my life in his hands.

All went well! The nurses couldn't believe how good I was doing.

Three days after arriving home, however, a pulmonary embolism returned me to the hospital for two more weeks. With that finally behind me recovery progressed nicely. After two and a half months I went back to work and tried to get into the swing of things. Somehow, things were **never** the same again.

Even though I felt that God had been a very big part of getting me safely through this experience, I began wondering why He had allowed it to happen, why He hadn't done something sooner if He was going to help me anyway, and why He had spared me. And I had other questions, too. Could this have been prevented? Could I have done something that caused this? These questions nagged at me for months to come.

Fibromyalgia

During this whole time Karen was my personal Rock of Gibraltar. I could count on her to take care of everything. She took care of the kids and their schoolwork, maintained the household, and kept the office going by arranging for other orthodontists to come in and cover the schedule. Needless to say, her stress level was high, especially at the beginning, not knowing the outcome of the surgery.

She began having mild muscle and joint soreness for no apparent reason as well as migraine-type headaches. Over time these symptoms became more severe and more frequent. Different medications were tried with no success. She was finally diagnosed with fibromyalgia. Stress commonly contributes to the etiology of this disease. She was told, "the good news is: it's not fatal. The bad news is: you'll wish you were dead." We were told there is no cure. Karen never knew from one day to the next how she would be feeling; sometimes better, sometimes worse. It became a very frustrating time for both of us dealing with this problem that just wouldn't go away.

Even though she felt God had been with us during this time,

she began thinking He must not like her since He had allowed all these bad things to happen. And how could He be a God of love if He allowed this pain to invade a person's life? Did God put us here to live the last half of our lives in pain and suffering and then die of some terrible disease?

We were both ready to begin our study!

* * * * * * * * * * *

14 I will praise thee; for I am fearfully and wonderfully made: marvelous are thy works; and that my soul knoweth right well.

(Psalm 139:14)

The Creator of man has arranged the living machinery of our bodies. Every function is wonderfully and wisely made. And God pledged Himself to keep this human machinery in healthful action if the human agent will obey His laws and cooperate with God. Every law governing the human machinery is to be considered just as truly divine in origin, in character, and in importance as the word of God. Every careless, inattentive action, any abuse put upon the Lord's wonderful mechanism, by disregarding His specified laws in the human habitation, is a violation of God's law. We may behold and admire the work of God in the natural world, but the human habitation is the most wonderful.   *(E.G. White manuscript files* 3)

(Counsels on Diet and Foods, p. 17)

Chapter Two

Our Study

The Juiceman

"Bill, you ought to see this! Come and watch with me." Karen called to me from the TV room. She had the TV on and when I walked into the room, an infomercial, of all things, was starting. This really wasn't on my list of things to do that day, but something about the way it sounded peaked my interest. Jay "The Juiceman" Kordich was beginning his pitch on juicing fresh fruits and vegetables. During his talk he mentioned "live" food and "dead" food. We had never heard that distinction made before. After hearing the whole commercial, we were convinced! We went out the same day to purchase a Juiceman juicer. Included in that purchase was an audio tape explaining even further about the benefits of juicing fresh fruits and vegetables. Jay also mentioned Dr. Norman Walker, his mentor and the "grandfather of juicing" who wrote several books about fresh juices and a "live" food diet. After juicing quite heavily for a couple of months, we started noticing we were feeling better, had more energy, and the aches and pains were disappearing. Karen's fibromyalgia symptoms were also improving; some days she felt almost normal! We were becoming so dedicated to this now that we located Dr. Walker's books and began what would turn into an in-depth study of diet and nutrition.

The Vegetarian Society

Shortly after reading six books by Dr. Walker, a picture in the newspaper of two people standing by a juicer caught our eye. The accompanying article explained that this couple was starting a Vegetarian Society in our town and it mentioned they juiced fresh fruits and vegetables. We had been wanting to meet other "juicers" for some time now so this seemed like an ideal way to do that.

Lin and Bj were suddenly an important part of our learning experience. Our first visit to the Vegetarian Society's monthly gathering proved to be just what we needed. After the evening's presentation an opportunity arose to meet these two people and the four of us hit it off immediately. We seemed to be on the same wavelength and a very close, lifetime friendship developed from that initial meeting.

They encouraged us to continue studying and suggested more books to read that continued our search. By the time the dust settled we had read at least fifteen books and numerous articles, seen several videos, and attended many lectures on diet and nutrition. Needless to say, we had reached some very definite conclusions about what to eat and how to prepare it.

With our Adventist background and superficial knowledge of the health message, something began "nagging" at us during this intense time of study. Soon this nagging became several great big questions.

* * * * * * * * * * *

15 Study to shew thyself approved unto God, a workman that needeth not to be ashamed, rightly dividing the word of truth. (*II Timothy* 2:15)

So closely is health related to our happiness, that we cannot have the latter without the former. A practical knowledge of the science of human life is necessary in order to glorify God in our bodies. It is therefore of the highest importance that among the studies selected for childhood, physiology should occupy the first place. How few know anything about the structure and functions of their own bodies and of natures laws! Many are drifting about without knowledge, like a ship at sea without compass or anchor; and what is more, they are not interested to learn how to keep their bodies in a healthy condition and prevent disease. (*Counsels on Health* p. 38)

Chapter Three

Our Questions

What does the Bible say about diet?

Somehow we had never thought about the Bible saying much about diet except for telling us as Adventists which meats we could and could not eat. How wrong we were! The first clinical trial comparing a vegan (Webster: a strict vegetarian who consumes no animal food or dairy products) diet to a meat-based diet is recorded in the Bible. Let's see how it started.

> 8 But Daniel purposed in his heart that he would not defile himself with the portion of the king's meat, nor with the wine which he drank: therefore he requested of the prince of the eunuchs that he might not defile himself. (*Daniel* 1:8)

Doesn't it sound like Daniel had come to some very definite conclusions about what he should eat and drink? So what does he suggest?

> 11 Then said Daniel to Melzar, whom the prince
> of the eunuchs had set over Daniel, Hananiah,
> Mishael, and Azariah,
> 12 Prove thy servants, I beseech thee, ten days;
> and let them give us pulse to eat, and water to drink
> 13 Then let our countenances be looked upon
> before thee, and the countenance of the children
> that eat of the portion of the king's meat: and as
> thou seest, deal with thy servants.
> 14 So he consented to them in this matter, and
> proved them ten days.   (*Daniel* 1:11-14)

The trial is now under way. Water and vegetables versus the king's meat and only ten days to prove his point! What was the result in ten days?

> 15 And at the end of ten days their countenances
> appeared fairer and fatter in flesh than all the child-
> ren which did eat the portion of the king's meat.
> 16 Thus Melzar took away the portion of their
> meat, and the wine that they should drink; and gave
> them pulse.   (*Daniel* 1:15,16)

So far so good! They looked better anyway, but they were in a three year training program for the king. Were the ten days just a fluke?

> 18 Now at the end of the days that the king had
> said he should bring them in, then the prince of the
> eunuchs brought them in before Nebuchadnezzar.
> 19 And the king communed with them; and
> among them all was found none like Daniel,
> Hananiah, Mishael, and Azariah: therefore stood
> they before the king.
> 20 And in all matters of wisdom and under-

standing, that the king inquired of them, he
found them ten times better than all the magicians
and astrologers that were in all his realm.
(*Daniel* 1:18-20)

I think we can safely say that the vegan diet in this first trial
was definitely better, at least regarding mental capability. Because of the correlation between mental health and physical
health, an assumption can also be made that they must have
been in the very best of physical health. Verse 19 states that
".....and among them all was found none like Daniel, Hananiah,
Mishael, and Azariah." The *Seventh Day Adventist Bible Commentary* indicates their physical strength and beauty were much
better than the others, so assuming them to be in excellent
health is a logical conclusion. All modern day studies between
these two lifestyles show, from a health standpoint, the superi-
ority of a vegan diet. None of the studies we saw compared
mental ability, but I suspect we would find it better also. Dr.
Dean Ornish of the Preventive Medicine Research Institute in a
very recent study has shown reversal of heart disease while
maintaining an almost pure vegan diet. Since this lifestyle will
reverse heart disease, is it not logical to assume that if we maintained a vegan lifestyle our entire life, we would never have
heart disease? (Or any other degenerative diseases?) As Adventists, we have known this for over one hundred years! We
really don't need any modern day studies to tell us what is best
for our body temples. God gave us a blueprint to follow not
only for our spiritual well-being, but also for our physical well-
being. It's called the Bible.

Is it possible that Daniel's lifestyle choices are to be used as
an example for those living in the end time, the same as his
prophecies?

Since meat was part of this first trial, let's look at some of the things the Bible says about meat eating.

> 3 Every moving thing that liveth shall be meat
> for you; even as the green herb have I given you
> all things.   (*Genesis* 9:3)

So God gave permission to eat meat right after the flood. The *Seventh Day Adventist Bible Commentary* states that Noah was aware of the difference between clean and unclean meats so that wasn't spelled out at this time. This information, however, was lost through succeeding years so subsequently had to be given in detail to Moses. (*Leviticus* 11)

> 4 But flesh with the life thereof, which is the
> blood thereof, shall ye not eat.   (*Genesis* 9:4)

The very next verse God places a stipulation on meat eating. Eat no blood.

> 17 It shall be a perpetual statute for your
> generations throughout all your dwellings, that ye
> eat neither fat nor blood.   (*Leviticus* 3:17)

A second stipulation was placed on meat eating. Eat no fat.

Thinking back to when I was a meat eater, it seems that it was the blood and fat that gave meat the flavor. If, when butchered, you could drain as much blood out as possible then somehow cook all the fat and remaining blood out of your burger or steak, I suspect it would be tougher than an old leather shoe and probably taste about the same!

Did God really want us eating meat?

God gave our first parents the food He designed
that the race should eat. It was contrary to His plan
to have the life of any creature taken. There was to
be no death in Eden. The fruit of the trees in the
garden, was the food man's wants required.
(Spiritual Gifts IV, 120)
(Counsels on Diet and Foods, p. 81)

Let's look at another example from the Bible concerning the
effects of diet as told by Ellen White.

The diet appointed man in the beginning did
not include animal food. Not till after the flood,
when every green thing on the earth had been
destroyed, did man receive permission to eat flesh.

In choosing man's food in Eden, the Lord
showed what was the best diet; in the choice made
for Israel, He taught the same lesson. He brought
the Israelites out of Egypt, and undertook their
training, that they might be a people for His own
possession. Through them He desired to bless and
teach the world. He provided them with the food
best adapted for this purpose, not flesh, but manna,
"the bread of heaven." It was only because of their
discontent and their murmuring for the fleshpots of
Egypt that animal food was granted them, and this
only for a short time. Its use brought disease and
death to thousands. Yet the restriction to a nonflesh
diet was never heartily accepted. It continued to be
the cause of discontent and murmuring, open or
secret, and it was not made permanent.

Upon their settlement in Canaan, the Israelites
were permitted the use of animal food, but under
careful restrictions, which tended to lessen the evil
results. The use of swine's flesh was prohibited,

as also of other animals and of birds and fish whose flesh was pronounced unclean. Of the meats permitted, the eating of the fat and the blood was strictly forbidden.

Only such animals could be used for food as were in good condition. No creature that was torn, that had died of itself or from which the blood had not been carefully drained, could be used as food.

By departing from the plan divinely appointed for their diet, the Israelites suffered great loss. They desired a flesh diet, and they reaped its results. They did not reach God's ideal of character or fulfill His purpose. The Lord "gave them their request, but sent leanness into their soul." They valued the earthly above the spiritual, and the sacred preeminence which was His purpose for them they did not attain.

(Ministry of Healing 311, 312)
(Counsels on Diet and Foods, p. 374, 375)

It seems that food has been a problem starting with our first parents and continuing down through the years to Israel's time and beyond. Is it possible this same scenario is being played out today in the Seventh-day Adventist Church?

The topic one night during Net 98 was "Darwin's Black Box," a discussion by Dwight Nelson on creation vs. evolution. Something he said that night caused me to look at the creation story in a different way. He called God the "Master Designer" and talked about how He had designed everything down to the smallest detail, then created it. In our world today the people that design and build a car, for example, know best what kind of fuel that car should use. Doesn't it stand to reason that God, who designed and created these wonderful body temples we inhabit, knows best what kind of food (fuel) they should use, too?

29 And God said, Behold, I have given you every
herb bearing seed, which is upon the face of all the
earth, and every tree, in the which is the fruit of a
tree yielding seed; to you it shall be for meat.
(*Genesis* 1:29)

18 Thorns also and thistles shall it bring forth to
thee; and thou shalt eat the herb of the field.
(*Genesis* 3:18)

After sin entered the Garden of Eden and Adam and Eve
were expelled, the "herb of the field" (vegetables) were added
to their diet. Because of sin we are now physically smaller,
weaker and less healthy than our original parents, but our basic
structure and genetic code are the same. (Unless, of course, you
believe in evolution!) With that said, it therefore seems logical
to me that the original diet given by God to man is still the best.

Was there a stove in the Garden of Eden?

What does Ellen White say about diet?

The first page (p. 481) of the appendix in *Counsels on Diet
and Foods* gives us an excellent place to start when considering
her advice. She discussed **so much** pertinent information concerning this subject for over forty years that it would be impossible to cover every point in a book such as this. But we will try
to cover what might be considered the main areas of concern.

[In reading the statements from Mrs. Whites
pen regarding her dietetic practices, the thoughtful
student will recognize the following principles:

First: "The diet reform should be progressive."
—*M.H.* 320. The light was not given in its fullness at the first. It was bestowed with increasing force from time to time as people were prepared to understand and act upon it, and it was fitted to the general practices and customs of eating at the time the instruction was given.

Second: "We do not mark out any precise line to be followed in diet."—*9T* 159. Repeated warnings were given against certain specific injurious foods. But in the main, general principles were laid down, and detailed application of these broad principles must sometimes be determined by experimentation, and by the best scientific conclusions available.

Third: "I make myself a criterion for no one else."—*Letter 45*, 1903. Having by intelligent experimentation adopted certain rules for herself, Mrs. White at times described the dietetic regimen of her own home, but not as a rule by which others must be rigidly governed.—**Compilers.**]

At the time she was writing, science knew very little or nothing about vitamins, minerals, enzymes, phytochemicals and the other substances, some still undiscovered, that feed us. How did she know then what was good and what was bad? Without the scientific evidence that we have today, I'm sure it was difficult to understand and accept some of these "radical" ideas she was embracing. Therefore, the diet reform was to be progressive. In other words, step by step we need to be striving for the best health practices and diet for our body temples, as time and evidence dictate.

The broad principles she believed in for increased health and longevity were pure water, pure air, sunlight, proper rest, proper diet, exercise, abstemiousness, and trust in Divine power. To study all of these areas is much more than a lifetime work and until we reach heaven will not be fully understood. Proper diet, in and of itself, is a continual learning experience. The scientific evidence today supporting all these principles is much broader and more in depth; it gives us more insight into what we should do and why. This, coupled with our belief in God and His Word, should lead us through individual study to His plan for us.

Ellen White did not dictate a certain diet for everybody. Through "intelligent experimentation" she adopted certain rules for herself. It behooves each of us to study individually and adopt our own rules.

The importance of this health reform cannot be overstated. She expressed this many times and in many ways.

> The health reform, I was shown, is a part of the third angel's message, and is just as closely connected with it as are the arm and hand with the human body. I saw that we as a people must make an advance move in this great work. Ministers and people must act in concert.
> (*Testimonies For The Church*, Vol. 1, p.486)
> (*Counsels on Diet and Foods*, p. 32)

> The controlling power of appetite will prove the ruin of thousands, when, if they had conquered on this point, they would have had moral power to gain the victory over every other temptation of Satan. But those who are slaves to appetite will fail in perfecting Christian character. The continual transgression of man for six thousand years has brought sickness, pain, and death as its fruits. And as we near the close of time, Satan's temptation to indulge appetite will be more powerful and more difficult to overcome. (*Counsels on Diet and Foods*, p.59)
> (*Testimonies For The Church*, Vol. 9, p.166)

What more can be said except that there are hundreds of other statements by her all pointing to the fact that this is something to be dealt with very seriously!

It is a duty to know how to preserve the body in the very best condition of health, and it is a sacred duty to live up to the light which God has graciously given. If we close our eyes to the light for fear we shall see our wrongs, which we are unwilling to forsake, our sins are not lessened, but increased. If light is turned from in one case, it will be disregarded in another. It is just as much sin to violate the laws of our being as to break one of the ten commandments, for we cannot do either without breaking God's law. We cannot love the Lord with all our heart, mind, soul, and strength while we are loving our appetites, our tastes, a great deal better than we love the Lord. We are daily lessening our strength to glorify God, when He requires all our strength, all our mind. By our wrong habits we are lessening our hold on life, and yet professing to be Christ's followers, preparing for the finishing touch of immortality.

My brother and sister, you have a work to do which no one can do for you. Awake from your lethargy, and Christ shall give you life. Change your course of living, your eating, your drinking, and your working. While you pursue the course you have been following for years, you cannot clearly discern sacred and eternal things. Your sensibilities are blunted, and your intellect beclouded. You have not been growing in grace and in the knowledge of the truth as was your privilege.

You have not been increasing in spirituality, but
growing more and more darkened.
   (*Testimonies For The Church, Vol. 2, p.70*, 71)
      (*Counsels on Diet and Foods*, p. 44, 45)

Man was the crowning act of the creation of
God, made in the image of God, and designed to
be a counterpart of God....Man is very dear to God,
because he was formed in His own image. This
fact should impress us with the importance of
teaching by precept and example the sin of defiling,
by the indulgence of appetite or by any other sinful
practice, the body which is designed to represent
God to the world.
   (*Review and Herald,* June 18, 1895)
      (*Counsels on Diet and Foods*, p. 45)

Was she shown these things for a reason?

What ever happened to the S. D. A. Health Message?

By this time we were looking back on the eating practices of
our lifetimes and remembering social events with family and
friends. Our diet during those years fit in perfectly with what
everybody else was doing, even the "worldly" people all around
us. Then, we read the following statement from the pen of
Ellen White during our reading of *Counsels on Diet and Foods.*

> Our habits of eating and drinking show whether
> we are of the world or among the number whom the
> Lord by His mighty cleaver of truth has separated
> from the world.
> *(Testimonies For The Church,* Vol. 6, p.372)
> *(Counsels on Diet and Foods,* p. 58)

Having never read this book before, we were shocked by some statements, surprised at others, and amazed that what she was saying seemed to point in the same direction we were going with our diet. Why hadn't we heard any of this before? This made us realize even more that this is an individual work. We better not wait for somebody else to figure these things out for us! We had always heard, "yes, there will come a time when we should give up meat," but unknown to us was the following statement written in the year 1902.

> When will those who know the truth take their
> stand on the side of right principles for time and for
> eternity? When will they be true to the principles
> of health reform? When will they learn that it is
> dangerous to use flesh meat? I am instructed to say
> that if ever meat eating were safe, it is not safe now.
> *(E. G. White manuscript files,* 133)
> *(Counsels on Diet and Foods,* p. 384)

We came to the conclusion to give up all animal products and go to a vegan diet after reading a secular book, *Diet for a New America* by John Robbins, which relied heavily on scientific evidence and known fact to prove his points. While all the time right under our noses were books written decades ago telling us to do the same thing and we hadn't bothered to study them! Is this what happened to the S.D.A. Health Message? **Apathy** on the part of everyone, including church leadership, from top to bottom?

Let me refer to Net 98 again and an evening when the topic was about traditions. Dwight Nelson talked about the reformation and some of the famous reformers from which different churches sprang up. He wondered why those churches had never advanced beyond the reforms in which these men believed. To answer that question he used the term "fenced in," meaning the thoughts of these different reformers were taken as the last word on the subject and the believers never studied or grew past the original beliefs. Could it be that the S.D.A. Health Message was "fenced in" at some point by an apathetic church body and never progressed beyond that point and actually appears to have regressed?

Or could it be that the membership of the church didn't (and still doesn't) want to look **that different** from the rest of the world?

Only personal study will answer these questions for you, but we believe there are good answers. We also believe there are good reasons for believing in a revived S.D.A. Health Message.

Why was the S.D.A. Church given the health message?

* * * * * * * * * * *

16 Know ye not that ye are the temple of God, and that the Spirit of God dwelleth in you?
17 If any man defile the temple of God, him shall God destroy; for the temple of God is holy, which temple ye are. (*I Corinthians* 3:16, 17)

Many have done the body much injury by a disregard of the laws of life, and they may never recover from the effects of their neglect; but even now they may repent and be converted. Man has tried to be wiser than God. He has become a law unto himself. God calls upon us to give attention to His requirements, no longer to dishonor Him by dwarfing the physical, mental, and spiritual capabilities. Premature decay and death are the result of walking away from God to follow the ways of the world. He who indulges self must bear the penalty. In the judgment we shall see how seriously God regards the violation of the laws of health. Then, as we take a retrospective view of our course of action, we shall see what knowledge of God we might have gained, what noble characters we might have formed, if we had taken the Bible as our counselor.

(E.G. White manuscript files, Letter 135)
(Counsels on Diet and Foods, p. 40)

Chapter Four

Our Reasons

SOME of our Biblical reasons for believing in the S.D.A. Health Message

In the previous chapter we discussed several things the Bible says about diet and health. Each of those examples could be included in this section, so be sure to review and study as necessary along with the following examples.

> 19 What? know ye not that your body is the
> temple of the Holy Ghost which is in you, which
> ye have of God, and ye are not your own?
> 20 For ye are bought with a price: therefore
> glorify God in your body, and in your spirit, which
> are God's. (*I Corinthians* 6:19,20)

This verse is very similar to *I Corinthians* 3:16,17 which was quoted at the end of the previous chapter. When we were growing up, these verses were used often to remind us that

smoking and drinking were bad for us and our health.   Sure
enough, forty or so years ago a link was established between
smoking and lung cancer.   More recently, a link has been established between the food we eat and various other cancers and
degenerative diseases. Is it possible to defile our bodies with
"food" as well as with other evil substances?   Let's see what
the *S.D.A. Bible Commentary* has to say about *I Corinthians*
6:19,20.

Temple. Because our bodies are the members of
Christ and temples of the Holy Spirit, which is given
to us by God, every sin that is committed against our
bodies is a sin against our Maker and against the
Holy Spirit.

Not your own. Man does not belong to himself;
he has no right to use his powers according to the
wishes and promptings of his unconverted body.
He is the property of God by creation and by
redemption. Man is bound to live mentally,
physically, and spiritually as God directs, to the
glory of His name, and not to the gratification of
fleshly desires. The converted man is, indeed, a
willing slave of Jesus Christ, who lives only to
please his Master.

Price. God evaluates the human race highly, as
shown by the fact that He paid an infinite price for
man's redemption. This fact reveals the importance
of each individual human being. Jesus would have
come to the earth and given His life for one sinner.
Being thus purchased by God, the redeemed sinner
is morally obligated to live for God only, to obey
all His commands, and to "flee" from all forms of
licentiousness.

In your body. Because men have been
redeemed from eternal death, it is their duty to do

all in their power to keep their bodies in the best condition, so that they may best glorify God by serving Him acceptably. An understanding of physiology, anatomy, and the laws of health is necessary if the body is to be taken care of intelligently. Christ's followers will not permit bodily appetites and desires to control them. Instead, they will make their bodies servants to regenerated minds that are constantly guided by divine wisdom.
(*S.D.A. Bible Commentary* Vol. 6 p.703)

The commentary breaks *I Corinthians* 6:19,20 into four parts as described above. Since the Holy Spirit dwells in our body temple and our redemption was purchased by an infinite price, we are "morally obligated to live for God only." This includes having an understanding of anatomy, physiology, and the laws of health, and then controlling our appetites and desires in order to be guided by divine wisdom.

Let's look at two verses in Romans that point out the need of maintaining the best health and avoiding worldly customs and traditions.

1 I beseech you therefore, brethren, by the mercies of God, that ye present your bodies a living sacrifice, holy, acceptable unto God, which is your reasonable service.
2 And be not conformed to this world: but be ye transformed by the renewing of your mind, that ye may prove what is that good, and acceptable, and perfect, will of God. (*Romans* 12:1,2)

We can study these verses, again, by using the *S.D.A. Bible Commentary* Vol. 6 p. 615, 616.

Your bodies. Paul first appeals to Christians to consecrate their bodies to God. He then calls on them to dedicate their intellectual and spiritual faculties (v.2). True sanctification is the dedication of the entire being-body, mind, and soul (*I Thess.* 5:23); the harmonious development of the physical, mental, and spiritual powers, until the image of God, in which man was originally created, is perfectly restored (*Col.* 3:10).

To a large degree the condition of the mind and soul depends upon the condition of the body. Therefore, it is essential that the physical powers be kept in the best possible health and vigor. Any harmful practice or selfish indulgence that lessens physical strength makes it more difficult for us to develop mentally and spiritually. Of this principle the adversary of souls is well aware, and he accordingly directs his temptations to the enfeebling and degrading of the physical nature.

The first part of verse 1 calls for us as Christians to consecrate our bodies to God. Since the condition of the mind and soul depends on the condition of the body, it is imperative that we maintain the physical health of our body temples.

A living sacrifice. The Christian sacrifice is of the living man. The Christian worshiper presents himself alive with all his energies and powers dedicated to the service of God.

Holy. Christians are to present their bodies in the best condition possible. All their faculties and powers must be preserved pure and holy, or else their dedication of themselves to God cannot be acceptable to Him.

This is no arbitrary requirement. God's purpose

for believers is their complete restoration. This
necessarily includes the purification and
strengthening of their physical as well as their
mental and spiritual powers. Therefore, the
Christian who by faith submits himself to God's
way of saving man will gladly obey this command
to regard the health of his body as a matter of the
highest importance. To do otherwise is to hinder
the divine work of restoration.

Further into verse 1 we find that the Christian sacrifice is of
the living man in which all aspects have been preserved pure
and holy. In submitting ourselves to God, by faith, we will
willingly obey this command to regard the health of the body as
a matter of highest importance.

Service. This verse attaches profound
significance to the principles of healthful living.
The believer performs an act of spiritual worship
by offering to God a holy and healthy body, along
with a consecrated mind and heart, because by so
doing he submits all there is of him to God's will,
and opens the way for the full restoration in him of
the divine image. It is an act of religious service to
preserve the physical powers in the best possible
condition. The reason is that the Christian glorifies
God in his body by serving as a living example of
God's saving grace and by participating with
increased strength and vigor in the work of
spreading the gospel. It was thus that the court of
Babylon beheld in Daniel and his companions "an
illustration of the goodness and beneficence of God,
and of the love of Christ." Their pure lives and
their outstanding development, physically, mentally, and spiritually, were a demonstration of what

God will do for those who yield themselves to Him
and who seek to accomplish His purpose.
(*S.D.A. Bible Commentary* Vol. 6 p. 615, 616)

Verse 1 closes with the admonition that "it is an act of religious service to preserve the physical powers in the best possible condition."

Verse 2 says we should not be conformed to this world and the *S.D.A. Bible Commentary* makes the following comments about that.

> **World.** The Christian must not go on following
> the fashion of this age, as was formerly his habit
> when he lived according to the flesh. On the
> contrary he must undergo a complete trans-
> formation by the renewing of his mind.
> (*S.D.A. Bible Commentary* Vol. 6 p. 616)

Since verse 1 is talking about the physical, mental, and spiritual condition of the body and verse 2 states not to do what the world is doing, should we be eating the way the world is eating if we want to maintain our bodies in the best physical, mental, and spiritual condition? No! In our personal experience the farther away we got from the way the world eats, the better we felt in physical, mental and spiritual ways.

We believe that there is yet another verse in the Bible that fits in here perfectly. More than likely this one will take much individual thought and study to come to the same conclusion, but it will be time well spent.

> 3 Thou shalt have no other gods before me.
> (*Exodus* 20:3)

We always looked at this commandment as meaning material possessions of some sort or some kind of idol. But could it also mean our controlling love of unnatural food that we know full well isn't good for us?

Another verse comes to mind that we have all heard at some point in time. Let's look in *I Corinthians* again. This book of *Corinthians* has been described as "one of the richest, most instructive, most powerful" of all Paul's letters.

> 31 Whether therefore ye eat, or drink, or
> whatsoever ye do, do all to the glory of God.
> *(I Corinthians* 10:31)

Whether. Paul sets forth a rule that is simple, easily understood, yet comprehensive, profound, and far reaching. Consciously and with unwavering determination the Christian must do everything, even the routine items of daily life, in such a way that God, not man, is honored. Such a course calls for constant dedication of all the powers of mind and body to Him, and daily surrender of all one's being to His Spirit.

Eat, or drink. Primarily, the application of eat or drink, is to the question of eating or drinking that which has any part in idol worship, but the admonition has a general application to food and drink of all kinds. Men are given the power of choice, but the Christian will exercise his choice at all times in a way that meets with the approval of God. Health must be protected as well as character. Food and drink are of major importance in relation to the preservation of health. Many illnesses that afflict mankind are due to errors in diet. God requires men to care for their bodies and to keep them fit to be temples of His Spirit. Hence, Christians must learn how to select food and drink that will not injure the body, but will promote

health, both mental and physical. The ancient
Israelites were assured that God would preserve
them in health if they would obey His instructions.
This He will do for His people now if they will
follow His counsel and take into their bodies only
those things that are in harmony with His laws.
**The Christian ideal is the original diet provided
by the Creator in Eden (Genesis 1:29).**
(emphasis-author)

Whatsoever ye do. The injunction is broadened
to include all the actions and plans of life. Christians are not at liberty to follow the promptings of
the natural, unconverted heart and the impulses of
the unregenerate body. They are under obligation
to bring every thought, word, and deed into harmony with Gods revealed will. The religion of
Christ concerns all the affairs of man, whether in
the physical, the mental, or the spiritual realm. The
redemption provided in Christ is a complete
redemption that applies to the entire man.

Glory. The Christians first motive in living in
harmony with the laws of God should be to promote
the honor of God. This motive arises from his love
for God and his desire to please his Maker. All the
energies of the soul should be used to advance the
interests of God's kingdom, and so to honor God.
(*S.D.A. Bible Commentary* Vol. 6 p. 750, 751)

Let's summarize the *S.D.A. Bible Commentary* on *I Corinthians* 10:31. As Christians, we will exercise our power of
choice to do **all** things to honor God, not man, and this includes
the food and drink taken into our bodies. We do this out of love
for God and our desire to please Him.

The final verse we want to study is found in the Old Testa-
ment book of *Hosea.*

6 My people are destroyed for lack of knowledge: because thou hast rejected knowledge, I will also reject thee, that thou shalt be no priest to me: seeing thou hast forgotten the law of thy God, I will also forget thy children.   (*Hosea* 4:6)

Once again, let's go to the *S.D.A. Bible Commentary.*

For lack of knowledge. The particular knowledge that is missing is the knowledge of God, the most essential of all knowledge. Isaiah ascribed the Captivity to such a lack. Though God may overlook certain forms of ignorance, He cannot condone deliberate ignorance of spiritual things. The people would inevitably be "destroyed" because of their lack of the essential knowledge. They might have had the knowledge had they put forth the effort to obtain it. Men are held responsible not only for what they know, but also for what they might have known had they put forth the effort to obtain essential knowledge. There are many who fear that a further investigation of truth will reveal that a change in conduct may be required of them, a change that their sin-loving hearts are unwilling to undertake, and so they deliberately desist from further inquiry. Such willful ignorance God cannot excuse.

Rejected knowledge. Literally, "rejected the knowledge." The priest, or perhaps rather the priestly order, is addressed.

No priest. This indicates that possibly the principal cause of this ignorance on the part of the people lay at the door of the unfaithful priests, who

rejected the knowledge of the true God and His law,
which they should have taught the people.
    (*S.D.A. Bible Commentary* Vol. 4 p. 898)

We find out in *Hosea* 4:6 that it is essential for us to put
forth effort to gain as much knowledge as possible about God.
He will not overlook deliberate ignorance of spiritual things. It
also suggests the possibility that at least part of the responsibility for any ignorance by the church members lays at the feet of
the church leadership.

Something else to consider in closing this section. What was
Satan's first temptation with Adam and Eve? What was Satan's
first temptation with Jesus at the end of His forty days in the
wilderness? What was the downfall of the Israelites? These
three questions can each be answered with all three of these
words: food, appetite, taste. Is Satan still using the same temptation that caused man's downfall? What factor contributed to
Daniel's and his three friends' health and superior intellect? Is
it possible that the diet God originally gave man will do for us
what it did for Daniel?

SOME of our Ellen White reasons for believing
in the S.D.A. Health message

The examples in the previous chapter could also be included
here; so, again, review and study as necessary along with the
following examples.

To make natural law plain, and to urge obedience to it, is a work that accompanies the third
angel's message. Ignorance is no excuse now for
the transgression of law. The light shines clearly,

and none need be ignorant; for the great God Himself is man's instructor. All are bound by the most sacred obligations to heed the sound philosophy and genuine experience which God is now giving them in reference to health reform.. He designs that the subject shall be agitated and the public mind deeply stirred to investigate it; for it is impossible for men and women, while under the power of sinful, health-destroying, brain-enervating habits, to appreciate sacred truth.

Those who are willing to inform themselves concerning the effect which sinful indulgence has upon the health and who begin the work of reform, even from selfish motives, may in so doing place themselves where the truth of God can reach their hearts. And, on the other hand, those who have been reached by the presentation of Scripture truth, are in a position where the conscience may be aroused upon the subject of health. They see and feel the necessity of breaking away from the tyrannizing habits and appetites which have ruled them so long. There are many who would receive the truths of God's word, their judgment having been convinced by the clearest evidence; but the carnal desires, clamoring for gratification, control the intellect, and they reject truth because it conflicts with their lustful desires. The minds of many take so low a level that God cannot work either for them or with them. The current of their thoughts must be changed, their moral sensibilities must be aroused, before they can feel the claims of God.

The apostle Paul exhorts the church, "I beseech you therefore, brethren, by the mercies of God, that ye present your bodies a living sacrifice, holy, acceptable unto God, which is your reasonable service." *Romans* 12:1. Sinful indulgence defiles the body and unfits men for spiritual worship. He who cherishes the light which God has given him upon health reform has an important aid in the work of becoming sanctified through the truth, and fitted for immortality. But if he disregards that light and lives in violation of natural law, he must pay the penalty; his spiritual powers are benumbed, and how can he perfect holiness in the fear of God?

Men have polluted the soul temple, and God calls upon them to awake and to strive with all their might to win back their God-given manhood. Nothing but the grace of God can convict and convert the heart; from Him alone can the slaves of custom obtain power to break the shackles that bind them. It is impossible for a man to present his body a living sacrifice, holy, acceptable to God, while continuing to indulge habits that are depriving him of physical, mental, and moral vigor. Again the apostle says, "Be not conformed to this world: but be ye transformed by the renewing of your mind, that ye may prove what is that good, and acceptable, and perfect, will of God." *Romans* 12:2   (*Counsels on Health* p. 21, 22, 23)

In this quote Ellen White points out that ignorance of God's natural laws is no longer an excuse because God Himself has become man's instructor. We should all be stirred to study and investigate this subject for ourselves because without health we cannot appreciate sacred truth. If our minds aren't on the highest plane possible, God cannot work either for us or with us. It is possible to arrive at the same conclusion concerning His natural laws by coming from either the presentation of Scripture truth or from health reform only, which in turn places the individual where the truth of God can reach their hearts. She then refers to *Romans* 12:1,2 and comments that whoever "cherishes the light which God has given him upon health reform has an important aid in the work of becoming sanctified through the truth, and fitted for immortality."

> Said the angel, "Abstain from fleshly lusts which war against the soul." You have stumbled at the health reform. It appears to you to be a needless appendix to the truth. It is not so; it is a part of the truth. Here is a work before you which will come closer and be more trying than anything which has yet been brought to bear upon you. While you hesitate and stand back, failing to lay hold upon the blessing which it is your privilege to receive, you suffer loss. You are stumbling over the very blessing which heaven has placed in your path to make progress less difficult. Satan presents this before you in the most objectionable light, that you may combat that which would prove the greatest benefit to you, which would be for your physical and spiritual health.
> *(Testimonies For The Church*, Vol. 1, p. 546)
> *(Counsels on Diet and Foods*, p.39)

The preceding comments clearly demonstrate that the health reform is a part of the truth but will be more trying than anything yet brought against us. Satan is still using appetite to deceive us into missing out on the blessing of health reform.

> When Satan takes possession of the mind, how soon the light and instruction that the Lord has graciously given, fade away, and have no force! How many frame excuses and make necessities which have no existence, to bear them up in their course of wrong, in setting aside the light and

trampling it underfoot. I speak with assurance. The greatest objection to health reform is that this people do not live it out; and yet they will gravely say they cannot live the health reform and preserve their strength.

We find in every such instance a good reason why they cannot live out the health reform. They do not live it out, and have never followed it strictly, therefore they cannot be benefited by it. Some fall into the error that because they discard meat, they have no need to supply its place with the best fruits and vegetables, prepared in their most natural state, free from grease and spices. If they would only skillfully arrange the bounties with which the Creator has surrounded them, parents and children with a clear conscience unitedly engaging in the work, they would enjoy simple food, and would then be able to speak understandingly of health reform. Those who have not been converted to health reform, and have never fully adopted it, are not judges of its benefits. Those who digress occasionally to gratify the taste in eating a fattened turkey or other flesh meats, pervert their appetites, and are not the ones to judge the benefits of the system of health reform. They are controlled by taste, not by principle.

(Testimonies For The Church, Vol. 2, p. 486, 487)
(Counsels on Diet and Foods, p. 398, 399)

She points out that when Satan takes control of the mind, the knowledge given to us by God fades away and has no force. We use numerous excuses for letting this happen and not live out the health reform. We should always be controlled by principle, not by taste. Those who have never adopted these ideals are not in a position to judge their benefits.

It is as truly a sin to violate the laws of our being as it is to break the ten commandments. To do either is to break God's laws. Those who transgress the law of God in their physical organism, will be inclined to violate the law of God spoken from Sinai.

Our Saviour warned His disciples that just prior to His second coming a state of things would exist very similar to that which preceded the flood. Eating and drinking would be carried to excess, and the world would be given up to pleasure. This state of things does exist at the present time. The world is largely given up to the indulgence of appetite; and the disposition to follow worldly customs will bring us into bondage to perverted habits; habits that will make us more and more like the doomed inhabitants of Sodom. I have wondered that the inhabitants of the earth were not destroyed, like the people of Sodom and Gomorrah. I see reason enough for the present state of degeneracy and mortality in the world. Blind passion controls reason, and every high consideration is, with many, sacrificed to lust.

To keep the body in a healthy condition, in order that all parts of the living machinery may act harmoniously, should be a study of our life. The children of God cannot glorify Him with sickly bodies or dwarfed minds. Those who indulge in any species of intemperance, either in eating or drinking, waste their physical energies and weaken moral power.

(*Christian Temperance and Bible Hygiene*, 53)
(*Counsels on Diet and Foods*, p. 17, 18)

In reading the previous quote we notice that violating the

"laws of our being" is the same as violating the ten commandment law. We were also warned that conditions in the world
near the end time would be similar to the days of Noah, with
eating and drinking carried to excess. She felt these conditions
existed during her time with indulgence of appetite and a pro-
pensity to follow worldly customs. What would she think if she
were alive today? To overcome these problems we need to
make the study of His natural laws an ongoing effort throughout
our lives.

Since the laws of nature are the laws of God, it
is plainly our duty to give these laws careful study.
We should study their requirements in regard to our
own bodies, and conform to them. Ignorance in
these things is sin.
"Know ye not that your bodies are the members
of Christ?" "What! know ye not that your body is
the temple of the Holy Ghost which is in you,
which ye have of God, and ye are not your own?
For ye are bought with a price; therefore glorify
God in your body and in your spirit, which are
God's." *I Corinthians* 6:15,19,20. Our bodies are
Christ's purchased property, and we are not at liberty to do with them as we please. Man has done
this. He has treated his body as if its laws had no
penalty. Through perverted appetite its organs and
powers have become enfeebled, diseased, and
crippled. And these results which Satan has
brought about by his own specious temptations, he
uses to taunt God with. He presents before God the
human body that Christ has purchased as His
property; and what an unsightly representation of
his Maker man is! Because man has sinned against

his body, and has corrupted his ways, God is dishonored.

When men and women are truly converted, they will conscientiously regard the laws of life that God has established in their being, thus seeking to avoid physical, mental, and moral feebleness. Obedience to these laws must be made a matter of personal duty. We ourselves must suffer the ills of violated law. We must answer to God for our habits and practices. Therefore, the question for us is not, "What will the world say?" but, "How shall I, claiming to be a Christian, treat the habitation God has given me? Shall I work for my highest temporal and spiritual good by keeping my body as a temple for the indwelling of the Holy Spirit, or shall I sacrifice myself to the world's ideas and practices?"

(Testimonies For The Church, Vol. 6, p. 369, 370)
(Counsels on Diet and Foods, p. 18, 19)

The above quote again stresses the importance of studying the laws of nature, which are the laws of God, because ignorance of them is sin. Our bodies were purchased by Christ at the Cross so they don't belong to us. It, therefore, behooves us to take the best possible care of our bodies while under our control. It is we ourselves who will suffer the ills of violated law, and we will answer to God for our habits and practices.

How did somebody with a third grade education know these things? Why was she shown these things? We, as Seventh-day Adventists, believe specific things, such as, the Seventh-day Sabbath, the third angel's message, and the health message based on what Ellen White was shown. Isn't it time we started to live the health message?

SOME of our scientific reasons for believing in the S.D.A. Health Message

Meat, Dairy, Eggs

Countless studies have been done on the effects of these so-called foods on the human body. One of the largest studies of this kind was conducted at Loma Linda University and involved more than 24,000 people. Reported in the *American Journal of Clinical Nutrition*, this study found the heart disease mortality rates for lacto-ovo vegetarians to be only **one-third** that of meat eaters. For vegans the very impressive figures were only **one-tenth** the heart disease death rate of meat eaters. Another study, mentioned previously, was done by Dr. Dean Ornish of the Preventive Medicine Research Institute in Sausalito, California. It shows reversal of heart disease on an almost pure (he allowed one cup of non-fat milk per day) vegan diet.

The China Health Project, one of the largest nutritional research projects ever conducted, documents that **in underdeveloped areas where populations consume predominately unrefined foods, the degenerative diseases of modern society as well as the leading cancers are virtually nonexistent.** The study confirms hundreds of other studies documenting that **most diseases of modern society originate from dietary folly.** The China Project dramatically demonstrates that if we plot the amount of animal foods eaten along with the death rates from the leading causes of death (heart disease and cancers), all animal food consumption, even fish and chicken, raises the rates of cancer and heart disease. Interestingly, even small quantities of animal foods in the diet were able to trigger higher cholesterol levels, heart disease and cancer.

The evidence from the China Project and other confirming

studies shows that the animal protein itself, not just the fat in the animal food, causes cholesterol and cancer to rise.

Cornell University's Dr. T. Colin Campbell, who headed the massive project, predicts that in the next ten to fifteen years research will solidly establish that animal protein is one of the most toxic nutrients for humans! "Whether industrialized societies can cure themselves of their meat addictions may ultimately be a greater factor in world health than all the doctors, health insurance policies, and drugs put together." (China Health Project summary-1983)

Howard Lyman, in his book *Mad Cowboy*, gives us the "plain truth from the cattle rancher who won't eat meat." The widespread use of antibiotics and hormones in the beef and dairy industry, as well as the feeding practices that could contribute to mad cow disease, pose a very real health risk to the individual who uses these products. (In addition to the previously mentioned problems shown in the China Project and other studies.)

The amount of dietary fiber has proven to be important as well. Meat, dairy, and eggs contain no fiber whatsoever; fiber is found only in fruits, vegetables, nuts, seeds and grains. A short transit time through our digestive tract, of all the food we eat, is ideal. Fiber acts as nature's broom to accomplish this for us.

We highly recommend reading *Diet for a New America* by John Robbins and *Mad Cowboy* by Howard Lyman. *Diet for a New America* has, literally, hundreds of references to articles and studies supporting a vegan lifestyle.

Processed Foods

Processed foods, such as cereal and pasta (anything in a bottle, box, can, or most packages), do not resemble in any way the food from which they were made. Most involve the use of heat in the processing and heat destroys all enzymes, which in turn adversely affects all vitamins, minerals, and any other nutrients found in that food. Invariably they have artificial chemicals and dyes included that are toxic to our bodies and injurious to our health. Processed foods usually have sugar or salt (or both!) added in order to entice us to eat them. Both sugar and salt in the forms added not only have no nutritional value but also have the same harmful effects as drugs!

Drugs

Webster defines a drug as "a substance other than food intended to affect the structure or function of the body of man or other animal." The body actually views all drugs as poisons, yet our society consumes approximately one billion pounds of drugs per year. Sixteen billion aspirin alone are consumed each year, but they don't heal anything. They just mask an underlying problem the body is trying to bring to our attention. Caffeine is also a drug that has become commonplace in our society. Even though these drugs aren't illegal, like cocaine and heroin, they still, over time, do much harm to our body temples.

Enzymes

In the introduction to *Enzyme Nutrition* by Dr. Edward Howell, Stephen Blauer says:

The study of food enzymes in nutrition and human health has been a "sore eye" to both scientists and nutritionists alike. For enzymes operate on both chemical and biological levels, and science cannot measure or synthesize their biological or life energy.

This biological force is the very core of every enzyme. Various names such as life energy, life force, life principle, vitality, vital force, strength, and nerve energy have been offered to describe this energy. Without the life energy of enzymes we would be nothing more than a pile of lifeless chemical substances—vitamins, minerals, water, and proteins. In both maintaining health and in healing, enzymes and only enzymes do the actual work. They **are** what we call in metabolism, the body's labor force.

Even though scientists can't agree on certain properties concerning enzymes, such as whether they are "alive" or just "active" substances or catalysts, it has been proven that heat does destroy their ability to do their job. The Master Designer placed them in our food for a reason, so whether the scientists agree or not on how they work or if they're "alive" or not does not matter to me. Just let them do their job the way He designed them to operate. With that said let's talk further about enzymes in general.

There are three types of enzymes: metabolic enzymes, which run our bodies; digestive enzymes, which digest our food; and food enzymes from raw foods, which start food digestion. Metabolic enzymes run every facet of our body, with every organ and tissue having its own specialized metabolic enzymes. The health of each of us depends on all of these metabolic enzymes doing the best job possible and the ability of the body to make enough of them. Without enzymes we would die!

Digestive enzymes do three jobs. They digest protein, carbohydrate, and fat.

God's plan calls for food enzymes (from raw foods) to start the digestive process and lighten the load on the body's digestive enzyme production, thus allowing the body to continue producing more of the all-important metabolic enzymes. Starting at 107 degrees Fahrenheit, heat starts to injure these food enzymes and by 130 degrees Fahrenheit **all** food enzymes are dead. This drastically alters the food by decreasing its nutritional content and eliminates the food enzyme help during digestion.

This brief summary is just the tip of the iceberg on enzymes. Please read *Enzyme Nutrition* by Dr. Edward Howell to get a much broader picture of this very important aspect of nutrition and health.

Isn't it clear our Master Designer put enzymes in our food for a reason? Should we destroy those enzymes before we eat that food?

* * * * * * * * * * *

8 Beware lest any man spoil you through philosophy and vain deceit, after the tradition of men, after the rudiments of the world, and not after Christr. (*Colossians* 2:8)

God has permitted the light of health reform to shine upon us in these last days, that by walking in the light we may escape many of the dangers to which we shall be exposed. Satan is working with great power to lead men to indulge appetite, gratify

inclination, and spend their days in heedless folly.
He presents attractions in a life of selfish enjoyment
and of sensual indulgence. Intemperance saps the
energies of both mind and body. He who is thus
overcome, has placed himself upon Satan's ground,
where he will be tempted and annoyed, and finally
controlled at pleasure by the enemy of all
righteousness.

(Christian Temperance and Bible Hygiene, 75)
(Counsels on Diet and Foods, p. 22, 23)

Chapter Five

Our Diet

What is food? According to Webster, food is "material consisting of carbohydrates, fats, proteins, and supplementary substances (as minerals, vitamins) that is taken or absorbed into the body of an organism in order to sustain growth, repair, and all vital processes and to furnish energy for all activity of the organism."

Where must this food ultimately end up to do its job? The body is segregated into several different "systems," but each of these systems have something in common. They are all made up of **cells!** It is in these trillions of cells where our health and very life is determined. Therefore, doesn't it make sense that we would want to give these cells the very best of whatever they need to survive and thrive?

One of the very first things the Master Designer told us was what to eat.

29 And God said, Behold, I have given you every
herb bearing seed, which is upon the face of all the

earth, and every tree, in the which is the fruit of a
tree yielding seed; to you it shall be for meat.
(Genesis 1:29)

Ellen White indicates we are being brought back to His
original plan. The following two quotes clearly show this.

In order to know what are the best foods, we
must study God's original plan for man's diet. He
who created man and who understands his needs
appointed Adam his food. *Genesis* 1:29. Upon
leaving Eden to gain his livelihood by tilling the
earth under the curse of sin, man received permission to eat also "the herb of the field."
Grains, fruits, nuts, and vegetables constitute
the diet chosen for us by our Creator. These foods,
prepared in as simple and natural a manner as
possible, are the most healthful and nourishing.
They impart a strength, a power of endurance, and
a vigor of intellect, that are not afforded by a more
complex and stimulating diet.
(Ministry of Healing, p. 295, 296)
(Counsels on Diet and Foods, p. 81)

The Lord intends to bring His people back to
live upon simple fruits, vegetables, and grains. . . .
God provided fruit in its natural state for our
first parents.
*(Extracts from Unpublished Testimonies in Regard to
Flesh Foods*, 5, 6)
(Counsels on Diet and Foods, p. 81)

In our study of this subject we started out with secular books
and first changed to a vegan lifestyle that included cooked food.
With additional study, again in secular books, we became con-

vinced that we should go to a **totally raw** (uncooked) vegan diet. It was about then that we began wondering about the Adventist health message and what Ellen White had said about diet and foods. We began our study into this aspect of the subject by reading *Counsels on Diet and Foods*. This in turn led us to the different Biblical lessons and texts, some of which we included in this discussion. Based on her statements and the Biblical examples, we now felt we were caring for our body temples more closely to God's plan and what He expects.

In actual practice this lifestyle has proven itself. Karen no longer has **any** symptoms of fibromyalgia and is leading a perfectly healthy life with none of the usual aches and pains of middle age. For ten years I dealt with some lingering problems left over from the aneurysm, and subsequent brain surgery, but since changing our diet most of them are gone and the few remaining ones significantly improved. Other problems common to middle age, like mild arthritis, have also disappeared.

We experienced very beneficial changes with our weight. It used to be a struggle keeping our weight in an acceptable range, and it seemed as though we had to move the range up every year or two to stay in it, in spite of dieting and trying to get plenty of exercise! We are both now back to our young adult weight and don't have to worry about any weight gain. Our bodies innately know what our ideal weight should be and, when given the proper food, will find and maintain that ideal weight. At the same time we have both experienced increased energy levels. All of these positive results with no calorie counting, no worrying about whether we're getting enough protein, too much fat, or enough vitamins and minerals. The Master Designer packaged our food for us with everything in it we need and in just the right amounts! We need only cooperate.

Our study into this subject has continued and in that process we have met or corresponded with other "raw foodists" from around the country. They have all experienced the same health benefits; some of them recovering from severe degenerative diseases! It works for everybody, Christian or not.

At the time of this writing we have been totally raw for over eighteen months and can't imagine how we could ever go back to our old way of eating. It became obvious to us after studying the texts in this book and Ellen White's insights into this subject that we had contributed in a major way to our health problems. **God** wasn't doing this to us; **we** were doing it to ourselves! He had actually given us guidelines to follow all along to prevent these health problems from occurring had we only been willing to follow them.

Let me close this chapter by asking an essential question: If we agree that **all** the nutrients known to man are **all** found only in fruits, vegetables, grains, nuts and seeds, what does cooking do to enhance the food value? Nothing!! In fact, cooking **diminishes** the nutritional value.

You don't have to be sick!

* * * * * * * * * * *

2 That thy way may be known upon earth, thy saving health among all nations.   (*Psalm* 67:2)

Physical habits have a great deal to do with the success of every individual. The more careful you are in your diet, the more simple and unstimulating the food that sustains the body in its harmonious action, the more clear will be your conception of duty. There needs to be a careful review of every habit, every practice, lest a morbid condition of the body shall cast a cloud upon everything.
(*Statement from E. G. White manuscript files*, 93)
(*Counsels on Diet and Foods*, p. 52)

Chapter Six

Our Truth

When people find out that we eat only raw fruits, vegetables, nuts, seeds and grains, the first question they invariably ask is, "How do you do that?" This question, we have found, means something different to each person asking it. Some people are really asking: how did you convert over to this new lifestyle from the previous lifestyle? From others it means: how or why have you maintained this new lifestyle? Yet another interpretation is: what do you do on a daily basis for your meals? These seem to be the three main areas of interest for most people, so we will try to express our thoughts on these questions. Keep in mind that this is an individual work and that there are countless studies in the world to support the philosophy of natural nutrition. What is amazing about this philosophy is that you can prove it conclusively true by your own experience! Until you have actually lived this lifestyle for a significant amount of time you are in no position to judge how good or bad it might be.

It was June of 1997 that we were sitting at the table in the breakfast nook of our home. Both of us had just finished reading several of Dr. Walker's books and we were discussing them.

We realized during that conversation that we should be eating our food just as it is grown—uncooked. Our first thoughts after coming to that conclusion were concerned with how we'd do that and especially how we'd avoid using bread! Even though we had decided that raw food was the best, we didn't convert over immediately. We continued reading and studying, only secular books at this time, and started eliminating the worst things from our table, such as dairy and egg products, white flour, and caffeine. (Several months prior to this conversation we had already eliminated all forms of meat from our diet.) As the unhealthful items disappeared, we added more and more raw foods of all kinds. As we progressed, we noticed our tastes were changing and we were feeling better. The cooked and processed foods became less appealing and the raw (uncooked) foods were more appetizing. We were also drinking one to one and a half quarts of fresh vegetable juice per person per day during this time.

In the fall of that same year we procured two books by George Malkmus. His books, *Why Christians Get Sick* and *God's Way to Ultimate Health*, were the first ones we had ever read giving a biblical perspective of an all raw diet. Here they were, written by a Baptist minister who seemed to have a more powerful health message than the Adventist church! It was now that we began wondering what Ellen White had to say about all this and what had happened to the S.D.A. health message. So we shifted the focus of our study to the Bible and Ellen White's writings.

December of 1997 brought the chance to travel two days by car to visit relatives and attend the wedding of a niece. This presented an opportunity to try a day of total raw food, so we loaded our ice chest with various fruits and vegetables, two quarts of fresh vegetable juices, and we threw in some raw nuts and headed down the road. We stopped only for gasoline and at roadside rests to stretch our legs and take care of life's other necessities. Twelve hours later we pulled into a motel and settled in for the night. During the day we ate when we felt like it and didn't try to stay with any kind of schedule. After arriving at the motel, we had a small supper of what was left of our raw vegetables and kept the remaining fruit for the following morning. We couldn't believe how much energy we had and how good we were feeling after our first totally raw day!

Shortly after returning home from that trip we did two totally raw days in a row and a few days later put together three raw days. We noticed that our tastes were continuing to change and that when we went back to eating the cooked food after being raw, we had a "heavy" feeling in our stomachs and our energy levels decreased. One day towards the end of February 1998 we finally decided to go totally raw. Since tradition and education have so ingrained in us many falsehoods about diet, a big part of making this change in lifestyle is a "mind game." To help in overcoming certain thoughts such as, "I'll never get to eat bread again," or "I can't go the rest of my life without some........," we decided on a three-month trial period. This seemed like a manageable time frame so we didn't have to think in terms of forever. We also decided that if for some reason we "cheated," we wouldn't let that halt the whole trial period.

Another part of why we decided to convert to raw food was the physical problems we were having. All of them had improved with the changes we had already made, but didn't seem to be improving very much any more. We wondered if a total change-over would further improve these problems, and better yet, help them go away once and for all. Quotes from Ellen White also entered into our decision. Some of them you have read earlier and they are in part: "Our habits of eating and drinking show whether we are of the world or among the number whom the Lord by His mighty cleaver of truth has separated from the world," and "again and again I have been shown that God is bringing His people back to His original design," and many others pointing to the importance of diet and our relationship to God.

The three months actually went by quite rapidly and by reminding ourselves of the above reasons, we managed to "cheat" **very** little and by the end of our trial period we were not "cheating" at all. Physically we were improving again and most problems were gone. There were days, however, that we didn't feel good and had what seemed like very little energy. This is part of the detoxifying process you go through as your body starts "cleaning house." After each of these "bad" days we bounced right back and felt better each time. Over the next several months these "bad" days came along less and less frequently and eventually disappeared completely.

The Master Designer gave us a wonderful healing mechanism that knows exactly what to do to make us well and keep us healthy. It just needs the proper building blocks in order to do the job, and it is our duty to make sure those "raw materials" are available. Remember, this is an individual work and each of us has to come to these conclusions for ourselves and put them into practice in a way that is comfortable for us personally.

At the end of our three-month trial period we were physically feeling much better. After evaluating all factors, including the amount of time we had invested in this new lifestyle, we decided to make this a permanent part of our lives. It was now easy to imagine the rest of our lives without bread and other cooked food items we had enjoyed so much in the past. It had become a real blessing in our lives.

Another aspect started becoming apparent to us also. Ellen White says it best. "When they break away from all health-destroying indulgences, they will have a clearer perception of what constitutes true godliness. A wonderful change will be seen in the religious experience." Much to our surprise this did prove to be true for both of us and we now felt like we were no longer just "going through the motions" in our spiritual lives, but rather we had found something more profound and life changing. This whole new lifestyle had now become part of our **core beliefs (truth)** and involved all aspects of our lives—phys-

ically, mentally, spiritually. How could we turn back now?
The following quote from Ellen White is another example, out of hundreds, that helped us come to this conclusion.

> Seventh-day Adventists are handling moment-
> ous truths. More than forty years ago (written 1909)
> the Lord gave us special light on health reform, but
> how are we walking in that light? How many have
> refused to live in harmony with the counsels of God!
> As a people, we should make advancement pro-
> portionate to the light received. It is our duty to
> understand and respect the principles of health
> reform. On the subject of temperance we should be
> in advance of all other people; and yet there are
> among us well-instructed members of the church,
> and even ministers of the gospel, who have little
> respect for the light that God has given upon this
> subject. They eat as they please, and work as they
> please.
> Let those who are teachers and leaders in our
> cause take their stand firmly on Bible ground in
> regard to health reform and give a straight testi-
> mony to those who believe we are living in the last
> days of this earth's history. A line of distinction
> must be drawn between those who serve God, and
> those who serve themselves.
> *(Testimonies For The Church*, Vol. 9, p.158)
> *(Counsels on Diet and Foods*, p. 24)

The above quote asks the question: "More than forty years ago (written 1909) the Lord gave us special light on health reform, but how are we walking in that light? Another fair question would be: Is the S.D.A. church as a whole, and each of us individually, really living up to the standard God expects of us? If we take an honest look, at ourselves and at those around us, how would we have to answer these two questions? In order to walk in this light the knowledge has to become part and parcel of how we live. Without an intimate understanding of the health message any progress toward reform will be short-lived. If we do not apply to our daily lives what we know to be true, are we really being honest to ourselves and to God?

It was during our study of George Malkmus' two books that we began to wonder about the S.D.A. church and its health message. Did the Bible say more about diet than we had been led to believe all our lives? Why weren't we hearing these things from our church—the only church, to our knowledge, that claims to have a health message? What did Ellen White really say about this subject? We had been praying that we would find an answer to our health problems and now a completely different door was opening up to us. Our prayers now centered on having guidance and help in understanding how all of this information fit into our whole life—physical, mental, and spiritual. Once the decision was made to go totally raw, faith became a **very** important factor. Considering the hundreds of years of tradition, the scientific confusion surrounding how the world eats today, and the peer pressure of family and friends, it is a real test of faith to step out and do something as "radical" as eating what our Master Designer told us to eat. Faith that what God said in the beginning would work, and prayer were the biggest parts of keeping us on this path.

We hope that by sharing some of our thoughts and experiences, it will give you a few ideas on how to go about this process for yourself. At the same time the first two questions, how did you convert over to this new lifestyle from the previous lifestyle and how or why have you maintained this new lifestyle, should have been answered. We'll begin to answer the third question, what do you do on a daily basis as far as your meals are concerned, by explaining a few things that happen as you begin to incorporate God's natural laws into your life.

In discussing cooked food with four different nutritionists

we got the same answer from each. Cooking destroys eighty percent of the nutrition in that food! (Could it be more?) Therefore, when we convert over to a raw food diet we actually end up eating less food because **the food we are now eating has one hundred percent of its nutrition in it.** This happens over time due to the fact that our body and mind have to adjust to these changes. Without the "full" feeling brought about by cooked food our brains misinterpret this as still being hungry, so at first we tend to eat more than is necessary. This is part of the "mind game" mentioned previously. As an interesting aside here, if cooking destroys eighty percent of the nutrition, doesn't it mean that eighty percent of the fuel, time, money, and effort spent on producing that food was also wasted? Plus the time involved with cooking it?

A typical day for us starts out with the juice of one-half lemon in an eight ounce glass of distilled water. We follow that with two to three ounces of freshly squeezed wheatgrass juice (one ounce equals in nourishment two and one-half pounds of vegetables). Shortly after this we'll have two to three pieces of seasonal fresh fruit and that will be all till lunch. Some days, shortly before lunch, we'll do an eight ounce glass of a fresh vegetable juice.

Lunch can take many forms, varying from one day to the next, with the most common being a very large green salad with every kind of chopped fresh vegetable in it that we have on hand. We also include a variety of sprouts including peas and beans, then top it off with a freshly-made, oil-less, raw avocado or cucumber dill dressing. We'll munch on some raw pecans, walnuts, or almonds along with the salad. Some lunches will be a raw room-temperature celery or vegetable soup or various other kinds of raw soup. In conjunction with the soup we will often times have a platter of raw vegetables. Other days just a large platter of our favorite vegetables and nuts with an avocado dip will suit our fancy.

Likewise, dinner varies from one day to the next. It can include any of the lunch items mentioned above or just be a sixteen ounce fresh fruit smoothie, or sometimes a raw entree of some sort. It just depends on what we feel like having, but the variety is surprising if you just think about it! This should give you some idea as to what a regular day of eating is for us, and there are actually non-cook books available such as, *Dining in the Raw*, that are full of tasty ideas. (Please refer to the resource list for more information.)

So, in a nutshell, it comes down to study, study, study. Read the examples in the Bible, previously discussed, and then read Ellen White's insights into the health reform. After this, look around you and see if you can't distinguish a difference between God's way and man's way. Take a close look at the animals in God's natural world. All of the animals living as God designed (in their natural state—untouched by man) still eat what God originally gave them to eat, and according to scientists the animals living under these conditions don't suffer from the degenerative diseases so common to man and the domesticated animals. Jesus is our ultimate example and in *The Desire of Ages* page 70 it states:

> "He who had made all things studied the lessons
> which His own hand had written in earth and sea
> and sky. Apart from the unholy ways of the world,
> He gathered stores of scientific knowledge from
> nature. He studied the life of plants and animals,
> and the life of man. From His earliest years He was
> possessed of one purpose; He lived to bless others.
> For this He found resources in nature; new ideas of
> ways and means flashed into His mind as He
> studied plant life and animal life.

God put into motion His natural laws at the beginning of earth's history and even put some of them into writing for our benefit. *The Desire of Ages* pages 50 and 51 tells us "........His physical structure was not marred by any defect; His body was strong and healthy. And throughout His lifetime He lived in conformity to nature's laws. Physically, as well as spiritually, He was an example of what God designed all humanity to be through obedience to His laws." The choice is ours! Either follow **all** His laws, both moral and natural, and reap the eternal rewards of obeying Him or ignore His laws, both moral and natural, and reap eternal death.

* * * * * * * * * * *

20 Incline thine ear unto my sayings.
22 For they are life unto those that find them, and health to all their flesh. (*Proverbs* 4: 20, 22)

I am instructed to bear a message to all our people on the subject of health reform; for many have backslidden from their former loyalty to health reform principles.

God's purpose for His children is that they shall grow up to the full stature of men and women in Christ. In order to do this, they must use aright every power of mind, soul, and body. They cannot afford to waste any mental or physical strength.

The question of how to preserve the health is one of primary importance. When we study this question in the fear of God, we shall learn that it is best, for both our physical and our spiritual advancement to observe simplicity in diet. Let us patiently study this question. We need knowledge and judgment in order to move wisely in this matter. Nature's laws are not to be resisted, but obeyed.

Those who have received instruction regarding the evils of the use of flesh foods, tea and coffee, and rich and unhealthful food preparations, and who are determined to make a covenant with God by sacrifice, will not continue to indulge their appetite for food that they know to be unhealthful. God demands that the appetites be cleansed, and that self-denial be practiced in regard to those things which are not good. This is a work that will have to be done before His people can stand before Him a perfected people.

(Testimonies For The Church, Vol. 9, p. 153, 154)
(Counsels on Diet and Foods, p. 36)

Chapter Seven

Our Hope

We believe this is a straightforward discussion on a very critical topic. Our intent is not to upset anyone, but to urge everybody, as members of the Seventh-day Adventist Church, to take a serious look at what is happening around us. Perhaps there is a better way—a better way that was shown to us back at the beginning of man's history and several times since then by various means.

The Bible is a book that was written for and directed to each and every one of us. It is a blueprint on how to live a spiritual life and how to get to know the God that created all things. It is also the best guideline available showing us what it takes to live a long and healthy life. Without health, the physical, mental and spiritual aspects of life just can't develop to the level God planned.

By studying the bible we can see how Satan has used appetite to deceive God's people from the beginning of earth's history. Starting with Adam and Eve, appetite has caused problems over and over again. The Israelites, whose leader was in direct communication with God, were shown the diet that was best for them, but due to appetite they failed to fulfill God's plan. Daniel insisted on not defiling his body with the king's meat and God used him in a powerful way! So powerful, in fact, that our church to this day depends on his writings to understand the times in which we live. Satan also used the power of appetite in tempting Jesus after His forty days in the wilderness. Because He overcame that temptation it has given us a chance at eternal life.

In modern times we find that the S.D.A. church was shown the health message through Ellen White. We have had this truth for over one hundred years now and during that time science has proven that everything Ellen White presented concerning diet is true. They have since discovered many more vitamins, all presently-known phytochemicals, and enzymes. They have also discovered that heat destroys a high percentage of the nutrition in our food. This fact alone points to the need for a simplicity of diet she so often discussed. It also coincides with her statements, such as, "The Lord intends to bring His people back to live upon simple fruits, vegetables, and grains." "Again and again I have been shown that God is bringing His people back to His original design," and "If ever there was a time when the diet should be of the most simple kind, it is now." Doesn't it then seem logical that Satan is still using this same temptation today? Could it be that Satan has hidden this temptation behind "science" with its confusion and disagreement over so many aspects of diet and nutrition? If science can't agree on many areas of this subject, why have we placed all our faith in them and their so-called knowledge? This is man's way and it seems to me God had a better way planned for us.

> We, as the representatives of Christ, are to meet every thrust of the enemy with the word of the living God. Never should we allow ourselves to follow the trail of the serpent by using his scientific arguments. Satan can never gain advantage of the

child of God who relies on the word of God as his defense.

Our Counselor impressed deeply on our minds that God's commandment-keeping people must be sanctified through the truth and that truth must ever be given the foremost place. We must not forget that Satan still lives to exercise his deceptive power through false science.

(*Testimonies For The Church*, Vol. 9, p. 68, 69)

The body has a built-in healing mechanism put there by the Master Designer and if we simply give it the proper building blocks, it will do a marvelous job of getting and keeping us healthy. If you are one of those who are eating the Standard American Diet (SAD), please take heart. Knowledge is power and with this book you have started your walk down a path to superior health and longevity. Don't take **our** word on this. There are countless studies in the world to support the philosophy of natural nutrition. But the most profound study is that which we conduct on our own body. What is amazing about this philosophy is that we can prove it conclusively true by our own experiences. Continue to study; then step out in faith that God's plan will work for you.

Ellen White said it over and over that our diet affects all aspects of our lives: the physical, the mental, and the spiritual. In practice we found this to be entirely true. The best way to describe it is to say that a change occurred in our spiritual lives, as well as our physical and mental lives, and we now feel a closer, more personal connection with our Creator and Master Designer.

God calls upon every church member to dedicate his life unreservedly to the Lord's service. He calls for decided reformation. All creation is groaning under the curse. God's people should place them-

selves where they will grow in grace, being sanctified, body, soul, and spirit, by the truth. When they break away from all health-destroying indulgences, they will have a clearer perception of what constitutes true godliness. **A wonderful change will be seen in the religious experience.** (emphasis-author)   (*Counsels on Health*, p. 579)
(*Counsels on Diet and Foods*, p. 34)

The brain nerves which communicate with the entire system are the only medium through which Heaven can communicate to man and affect his inmost life. Whatever disturbs the circulation of the electric currents in the nervous system lessens the strength of the vital powers, and the result is a deadening of the sensibilities of the mind.
(*Testimonies For The Church*, Vol. 2, p. 347)

No matter how well we maintain our health by applying the Biblical principles outlined in this book, we could still spend eternity separated from God and heaven. Let's not let this happen. We should put our faith in Christ, follow all His teachings, and look to the cross as our salvation. He came and died that we might be saved.

Our desire is that by putting these principles to work in our lives, we, as the Seventh-day Adventist Church, will become as a renewed light unto the whole world and finish this work that was given to us to complete so many years ago.

Our hope is that **very soon** a group will come forward willing to follow God's way and show the world that He truly is a God of love. He put in writing the information we need to live a long healthy life witnessing for Him. He also gave us a completely free power of choice. The choices we make every day in all walks of life are deciding our destiny. Isn't it time we make a commitment to live our lives in harmony with **all** aspects of God's final message to this world?

* * * * * * * * * * *

105 Thy word is a lamp unto my feet, and a light unto my path. (*Psalm* 119:105)

At the time the light of health reform dawned upon us, and since that time, the questions have come home every day, "Am I practicing true temperance in all things?" "Is my diet such as will bring me in a position where I can accomplish the greatest amount of good?" If we cannot answer these questions in the affirmative, we stand condemned before God, for He will hold us all responsible for the light which has shone upon our path. The time of ignorance God winked at, but as fast as light shines upon us, He requires us to change our health-destroying habits, and place ourselves in a right relation to physical laws.
(*Good Health*, November, 1880)
(*Counsels on Diet and Food*, p. 19, 20)

13 Enter ye in at the strait gate: for wide is the gate, and broad is the way, that leadeth to destruction, and many there be which go in thereat:

14 Because strait is the gate, and narrow is the
way, which leadeth unto life, and few there be that
find it.   (*Matthew* 7:13,14)

Those who elevate the standard as nearly as
they can to the order of God, according to the light
God has given them through His word and the
testimonies of His Spirit, will not change their
course of action to meet the wishes of their friends
or relatives, be they one or two or a host, who are
living contrary to God's wise arrangement. If we
move from principle in these things, if we observe
strict rules of diet, if as Christians we educate our
tastes after God's plan, we shall exert an influence
which will meet the mind of God. The question is,
"Are we willing to be true health reformers?"

(Letter 3, 1884)
(*Counsels on Diet and Foods*, p. 35)

RESOURCES

"Men dig their graves with their own teeth and die more by those fated instruments than the weapons of their enemies." Thomas Moffett   *Helth's Improvement*,
                                                                    1600 AD

Diet for a New America
John Robbins
Stillpoint Publishing
Box 640
Walpole, NH 03608
1-800-847-4014

God's Way to Ultimate Health
George Malkmus
Hallelujah Acres Publishing
P.O. Box 2388
Shelby, NC 28151
1-704-481-1700
www.hacres.com

Fresh Vegetable and Fruit Juices
Norman Walker
Norwalk Press
P.O. Box 12260
Prescott, AZ 86304
1-520-445-5567

Enzyme Nutrition
Edward Howell
Avery Publishing Group
Wayne, New Jersey
(can be purchased through Nature's
First Law)

Nature's First Law: The Raw-Food Diet
Arlin, Dini, Wolfe
Nature's First Law
P.O. Box 900202
San Diego, CA 92190
1-800-205-2350
www.rawfood.com

Counsels on Diet and Foods
Ellen White
Review and Herald
Publishing Assoc.
Takoma Park,
Washington, D.C.

"When Health is absent
Wisdom cannot reveal itself,
Art cannot become manifest,
Strength cannot be exerted,
Wealth is useless and
Reason is powerless."
                    Herophiles, 300 BC

Diet and Salad
Norman Walker
Norwalk Press
P.O. Box 12260
Prescott, AZ 86304
1-520-445-5567

Mad Cowboy
Howard F. Lyman
Scribner
1230 Avenue of the Americas
New York, NY 10020

The Wheatgrass Book
Ann Wigmore
Avery Publishing Group Inc.
Wayne, New Jersey
(can be purchased through Nature's First Law)

The Juiceman's Power of Juicing
Jay Kordich
William Morrow and Co.
1350 Ave. of the Americas
New York, NY 10019

Counsels on Health
Ellen White
Pacific Press Publishing
Association
Nampa, Idaho

Recipe Books

Dining in the Raw
Rita Romano
Kensington Publishing
850 Third Avenue
New York, NY 10022
(can be purchased through Nature's
First Law)

Angel Foods
Cherie Soria
Heartstar Productions
3911 Antone Rd.
Santa Barbara, CA
93110

Quick Order Form

Mail to: **North Idaho Publishing**
 P.O. Box 2833
 Coeur d'Alene, ID 83816-2833
 e-mail: bill--scott@msn.com
 www.williamscott.com

Name (please print) _____

Address _____

City _____ State _____ Zip _____

In The Beginning, God Said.
Eat Raw Food

Quantity Discounts		ID Sales Tax
One book,	$7.95	40 cents each
2 - 10 books,	$6.95 ea.	35 cents each
11 - 49 books,	$5.95 ea.	30 cents each
50 or more books,	$4.77 ea.	24 cents each

Please send me: _____
copies of "In The Beginning, God Said.
 Eat Raw Food" @ $ _____ = $ _____

sales tax (Idaho only) $ _____

shipping $ _____

Total $ _____

Make checks payable to **North Idaho Publishing**

Shipping and Handling: $3.00 for 1 book. $5.00 for 2-7 books. For orders of $50.00 or more, add 10% of order total.